Under the Apple Boughs

The Home Place
The Saskatchewan Suite

Donna McCaw
OASIS Publishing
Box 810, Elora, Ontario N0B 1S0
www.sentex.net/~dmccaw

Printed in Canada using Recycled Paper

OTHER WORKS BY
DONNA MCCAW

Sing a Song of Six Packs - 1996

Thirsty for Herstory - 1996

Spiral to the Heart - 1996

A Visit To Gramma's
I Remember Margaret
reprinted from *Spiral to the Heart*

Canadian Cataloguing in Publication Data
McCaw, Donna, 1949 -
    Under the Apple Boughs
ISBN 0-9680-683-2-4

Dedication

This book is dedicated to my father, Floyd George McCaw. He was a farmer who respected the land and his job of working with the forces and cycles of nature to make a good living for his family. He taught lessons of honesty and hard work, was a good neighbour and community member, as well as a great baseball player. The fact that he was a life-long Toronto Maple Leafs fan is one indication that he was a man of great patience. He was also a fine dancer who rarely missed an opportunity to attend community dances and card parties. He was the kind of man who built this country.

This book is also in memory of the many brave people who cleared and settled our country. At one time, over 90 per cent of Canada's people made their livelihood through agriculture.

This is also for those special people who still live and work on the land.

SPECIAL THANKS TO:

Robert Lyon, editor and friend, who gives his time and efforts so generously.

Penny Clemens at YDezign for her creative work.

Doug Hollingsworth for his unique cowboy-trucker-farmer poetry reprinted from *A Collection of Memories*.

And especially to Mom and Dad for the home place — and all that meant.

PERMISSION

The purpose of this little note
Is to tell the world it's true I wrote
"Feeding the Cats" and also the "Snipe"
And that I say it's quite alright
For Donna McCaw to include them somehow
In her book, "Under the Apple Bough(s)."

Doug Hollingsworth

FERN HILL

Now as I was young and easy under the apple boughs
About the lilting house and happy as the grass was green,
    The night above the dingle starry,
        Time let me hail and climb
    Golden in the heydays of his eyes,
And honoured among wagons I was prince of the apple towns
And once below a time I lordly had the trees and leaves
        Trail with daisies and barley
    Down the rivers of the windfall light.

And as I was green and carefree, famous among the barns
About the happy yard and singing as the farm was home,
    In the sun that is young once only,
        Time let me play and be
    Golden in the mercy of his means,
And green and golden I was huntsman and herdsman, the calves
Sang to my horn, the foxes on the hills barked clear and cold,
        And the sabbath rang slowly
    In the pebbles of the holy streams.

All the sun long it was running, it was lovely, the hay
Fields high as the house, the tunes from the chimneys, it was air
    And playing, lovely and watery
        And fire green as grass.
    And nightly under the simple stars
As I rode to sleep the owls were bearing the farm away,
All the moon long I heard, blessed among stables, the nightjars
        Flying with the ricks, and the horses
        Flashing into the dark.

And then to awake, and the farm, like a wanderer white
With the dew, come back, the cock on his shoulder: it was all
Shining, it was Adam and maiden,
The sky gathered again
And the sun grew round that very day.
So it must have been after the birth of the simple light
In the first, spinning place, the spellbound horses walking warm
Out of the whinnying green stable
On to the fields of praise.

And honoured among foxes and pheasants by the gay house
Under the new made clouds and happy as the heart was long,
In the sun born over and over,
I ran my heedless ways,
My wishes raced through the house-high hay
And nothing I cared, at my sky blue trades, that time allows
In all his tuneful turning so few and such morning songs
Before the children green and golden
Follow him out of grace,

Nothing I cared, in the lamb white days, that time would take me
Up to the swallow thronged loft by the shadow of my hand,
In the moon that is always rising,
Nor that riding to sleep
I should hear him fly with the high fields
And wake to the farm forever fled from the childless land.
Oh as I was young and easy in the mercy of his means,
Time held me green and dying
Though I sang in my chains like the sea.

Dylan Thomas

TABLE OF CONTENTS

THE HOME PLACE

THE SASKATCHEWAN SUITE

The
Home Place

THE FARM HAD BEEN IN THE FAMILY SINCE 1864. A long time for Canada. A century farm in 1967. A place to grow up with roots, memories, stories, and certainty. A place to be. A home for always.

A place to show the kids. Take them home. Let them know about childhood on the farm, about their family. Show them the calves in the spring, the garden as it grows, the wheat, the apple trees, the pond, and the corn knee high by the fourth of July and a great hiding place by fall.

Show them the one-room school, the iron pump, the long sliding hill, and the outhouses. Show them the wooden desks bolted to the floor, the ink wells, and the porcelain wash basin.

Take them to church. Listen to the old folks make a fuss over them.

Show them the pictures on the walls at the home place, the images of the hard-faced settlers, the pioneers, their great, great, grandparents.

Eat mashed potatoes, string beans and roast beef that never saw a supermarket. Taste homemade pie . . . fresh baked apple, rhubarb custard, elderberry.

Teach them to play euchre.

Wonder whether they will ever know that feeling of the home place.

"To be born on a farm is the greatest good
that can befall a human being."

Peter McArthur
"the Sage of Ekfrid", Middlesex County

From FOR HOME AND COUNTRY:
THE CENTENNIAL HISTORY OF THE WOMEN'S INSTITUTES
IN ONTARIO, 1997

"After her baby's death, Adelaide Hoodless devoted herself to a new cause: promoting domestic science education. The young Mrs. Hoodless was angry and disappointed that her own education had left her so ill-equiped to run a household without tragic consequences."

"The members themselves were the real backbone of the new Institute. The first president, Mrs. E.D. Smith, was described by her daughter Verna as a woman who was always deeply concerned with everything that lightened the drudgery and long hours of toil of the farmer's wife."

From OLDER VOICES AMONG US
edited by Alvin Koop and Sheila McMurrich Koop

"One old pioneer showed him an overturned stump where he and his father stayed all summer until they could build a shanty for themselves. Others even built wigwams like the Indians to live in."
about John Ord of Puslinch township

"The first thing I done was go out and get those cows in and start to milk. I'd call my sister and she'd get up. I used to get the cows in and milk nine cows by hand and she'd milk five. I'd feed my father's team of horses and get them ready for him to go on the road and he just got up and eat his breakfast and got away. Then I'd go and get my breakfast and that would be somewhere between six and half-past six in the morning. And then get another bunch of horses ready and get to the field — plough, cultivate or whatever was on the go."
Abe McComb of Minto township

From THE PEOPLE'S HOME LIBRARY, 1916
Dr. Ritter's Liniment - Take 2 ounces if camphor gum, 1 ounce of ammonia water, 1 ounce of turpentine, 3 ounces of sweet oil, 3 ounces of kerosene, 2 ounces of laudanum and 4 ounces of alcohol.

To curl feathers - When nearly dry draw each flue or fibre over the edge of a blunt knife, turning it the way you want it to curl.

Patent soap - Three pounds grease, three pints of salsoda, one-half pint turpentine, two pounds resin soap, forty gallons water; boil one hour.

Simple home remedies: salt, lemons, kerosene oil, borax.

FEEDING THE CATS

Now listen close, folks, and I'll tell you a story
Of something that happened to me when I was still a small boy.

I was raised in the sticks way out on a farm
We had cats and dogs and cows in the barn

Every morning it was a regular fact
That I had to feed those lazy cats.

I'd walk to the barn with a little pail of stuff
And pour it in their dish – it was never enough.

Those cats would meow and claw for a place
And I barely had time to get out of the way.

Every morning was like the morning before,
Those cats would line up and we'd do it once more.

But then one day when I was fooling around, (I dropped my
pail) and spilled the milk on the ground.

Uh oh, too bad. What to do now?
I wonder if *I* could milk Bessie the cow?

Could milking be hard? I couldn't see why.
Other people did it. I'll give it a try.

Now old Bessie's been around for many a day
With a long set of horns – one pointed each way.

Her udder was full, she had way too much
But the look in her eye said, "Better not touch!"

Well, I knew old Bessie could be downright mean,
But I was young and dumb and right full of beans.

So I got my lasso, threw with all my might
It went over Bessie's head and I snugged it up tight.

Well I caught old Bessie on the twenty-third throw,

Roping's not as easy as it looks in the show.

And for Bessie to stand there was too much to hope
So I called my sister Karen to hold onto the rope.

"Now hold on really tight and don't you let go
Cause I'm gonna milk that old cow don't you know."

Then I heard a meow and when I turned my head
There was the whole bunch of cats – waiting to be fed.

There was Mama and Papa and all of the kits
Just sitting there watching and licking their lips.

I walked over to Bessie and sat down beside
Her tail hit my face so hard I could cry.

But I was determined to do this thing right.
I was gonna milk Bessie if it took me till night.

I reached for her udder and gave it a touch
But I guess old Bessie didn't like it so much.

She gave me a kick – I thought my butt was broke.
And Karen laughed so hard I was afraid she might choke.

So I pulled myself up and I straightened my hat
And I said to old Bessie, "We'll have no more of that."

Then I pleaded with Bessie, "Please, can't you see
Those poor starving cats are counting on me?"

And I moved in much closer than ever before
Squeezed a bit of milk – then a little bit more.

And I was doing real good – I had almost enough
When Bessie looked around and things kinda got rough.

She jumped *straight* in the air and I fell to the ground

And my shiny little pail went round and round.

And the bit of milk went high in the air
It felt warm and sticky and wet everywhere.

There was lots of milk all over the place
From my head to my heels and all over my face.

And I though to myself, "Isn't this a nice pose?"
Me lying on the ground, milk dripping from my nose.

And over by the fence, as neat as could be
The whole bunch of cats were grinning at me.

It made me so mad – I was losing my cool
Why, that cow made me look like some kind of fool!

And worst of all, as far as I could see,
It looked like old Bessie was getting the best of me.

And Karen on the rope was splitting her sides
So I got to my feet and wiped the milk from my eyes.

And I vowed to myself, "I'll milk that old cow."
But what I hadn't figured was – just exactly how.

Then I got and idea that might work just fine
I'll tie her all up with a strong piece of twine.

So I got a long string and I wound it around
And I covered old Bessie from her head to the ground.

And all you could see when I tied the last rope
Was a long set of horns in a shaggy overcoat.

Her legs tied together, her tail fastened tight,
I'm sure that we must have been a strange looking sight.

Then I reached for her udder, I gave it a squish,
The milk flew out easy – there was nothing to this.

I filled my small pail in a minute or three,
And I stood beside Bessie as proud as could be.

And I yelled out to Karen, "Whenever you choose,
Let go of the rope and let her go loose."

The rope fell away – Bessie looked forlorn,
Bet she was wishing I was stuck on her horn!

But then she kicked at the fence with at terrible smack,
And ran to the pasture like she'd never be back.

And Karen said, "I thing that you did okay,
But it sure looks to me like the cats ran way."

And I saw she was right, they were nowhere to see,
Guess I was too slow and they gave up on me.

So there I was covered with dirt, flies and sweat,
With a small pail of milk that I'd worked hard to get.

But what could I do since the cats ran away?
Guess I might as well save it and use it next day.

And I learned a big lesson for the rest of my life,
Never worry about cats, let them go catch some mice.

Doug Hollingsworth

Farmyard Semantics and the Triumph of the Human Spirit

*"Before the children green and golden
Follow him out of grace,"*

MY SISTER AND BROTHER AND I went to a red brick one-room school house, S.S. #3 Metcalfe Township. We had a coal furnace, oiled floors, well water hauled daily from a pump outside, and two outhouses around the back — the boys' and the girls'. We all took turns bringing water in and out again, cleaning the boards, helping in the junior grades, and putting on the Christmas concert.

I was in grade five and my sister was in grade two when we learned a lesson in semantics. One day, my sister was gripping her pencil very hard and I could tell she was concentrating because the tip of her tongue was pointing out the right side of her mouth and her eyes were narrowed. She was making little circles between the big blue solid line and the pale blue broken one. These circles were supposed to just touch the "sticks" that went all the way up to the other solid line.

In the middle of executing one of these circles, my sister's lead broke and she went right outside of the line. Exasperated, she said out loud, "Oh, shit!" A hushed silence fell over the room and we waited anxiously for the teacher's response. We didn't wait long.

We lived on a farm where the words "shit" and "manure" were fairly interchangeable. Our teacher lived on a farm where that was not the case.

She lectured my sister, in front of everyone from grade one to eight, on the proper use of the word manure and the unacceptability of the "other word". She then imposed the worst punishment possible for my sister. She had to stay in at recess — the public humiliation of a seven year old.

My sister bore the shame, felt the anger and knew the injustice in silence. I was concerned for silence was not my sister's usual response to anything.

We rode home after school in Mr. P.'s station wagon that was our bus. My sister usually raced down the long lane to the house, but this day she dragged her feet in the dust, where her spirits appeared to be.

As soon as she saw our mother waiting for us in the kitchen , she began to sob loudly and uncontrollably. My mother looked at me questioningly as she held this sob-wracked child. I didn't know what to say. We waited until my sister, amid hiccups, snorts, and sighs, blurted out her story. When she got to the part about what she had said, my mother put her hand over her eyes, shook her head and said, "Oh, shit!"

The teacher went to the same church that we did, that everybody around there went to really. It was the Knox Presbyterian Church, the yellow brick one right down the hill from the school. Mom would have to face our teacher on Sunday with a seven year old who felt indignant, wronged, yet ashamed.

My mother had a little talk with my sister to try to explain about shit and manure and misunderstandings and about playing it safe. My sister seemed to understand the part about the family reputation and promised not to make a scene at church by telling God on the teacher. We had Saturday to forget the whole thing or so my mother hoped.

On Saturdays farm women baked. My mother and Mary, next door, were no exceptions. We did not yet have a television set but our neighbours, Bill and Mary, did. They were an older couple, childless and indulgent and generous to us. Every Saturday afternoon after lunch, my brother and sister and I would hike over our front field, climb over the wire fence, walk across Bill and Mary's front field to hot oatmeal cookies and cold glasses of milk.

We would have a visit with Mary, tell her all about school and what we were doing, and then we could watch Wagon Wheels, an exciting Western, and eat lots of cook-ies. I noticed this Saturday that my sister was quite quiet. Her eyes looked at me pleadingly not to tell the story of her shame to Mary. I respected her pleas.

During the first commercial, Bill came in to the sun-porch from the barn. We heard Mary yell from the kitchen, "Take off those damn boots and don't go tracking that shit over my clean floors!"

My sister straightened like a deer at the snap of a twig. She very seriously went into the kitchen, took Mary by the hand, and had a little talk with her about the proper use of the word 'manure'. I could see the look of disbelief on Mary's face and a little smile on her lips when she said, "You really don't believe that shit, do you?"

My sister immediately snapped back to her self-confident, some might say brash, self. Her spirit was no longer broken and her shame was cast aside. The next day was church.

The teacher was already seated in her family's pew when the five of us filed into ours. We sat through the most tedious hour imaginable. Mr. Kelly snored as usual, and we all gathered outside to visit after the service. The teacher gave my mother one of her little condescending smiles, and began the conversation that would once again humiliate my sister publicly.

Just then my sister marched up to the teacher and, in a loud, proud and defiant voice, announced to most of the congregation including the minister, "You know what, teacher? We talked about that manure stuff and we don't believe in that shit!"

My mother covered her eyes and shook her head and I knew just what she was thinking. Many of the others covered their mouths stifling horror or laughter, while my sister marched off, head held high in utter triumph!

MARY'S OATMEAL COOKIES

1 1/2 cp. Brown sugar	Mix.
1 1/2 cp. flour	Press on cookie sheet
1 1/2 cp. oatmeal	with wet fork.
1 cp. shortening	
1 egg	Bake at 325°F for 10 min-
1 tsp. baking pwdr.	utes and watch them.
1 tsp. salt	
1 tsp. baking soda	

Ghost Chasing

*"About the happy yard and singing
as the farm was home,"*

I T WAS THE NIGHT BEFORE HALLOWE'EN. It was that lovely
time between day and night, warm for October. I
remember that evening to this day. I was 8, my sister was
6 and my brother was 4. We were outside in the yard by
the back step trying to get the candles to stand up in our
carved pumpkins when, all of a sudden, a ghost flew right
by us!

For a brief moment, we were frozen with fear. Then
one of us yelled, "Let's get it!"

We started pumping our little legs in hot pursuit of

the white apparition, down the laneway, through the gate, and into the barnyard. The ghost went around the barn through the mud and we lost sight of it for an instant. When we rounded the corner of the barn, it had vanished!

We looked up, we looked all around, but it had evaporated into thin air! We looked all through the rusted piles of ancient machinery, through the apple orchard, and then went into the barn. My dad was feeding the animals.

"Dad, dad, did you see the ghost? Did it come in here?" we asked breathlessly.

He chuckled and looked at us very strangely. "Nope, no ghosts in here."

We searched the haymow and the pens and the barnyard, but no luck in locating the mysterious ghost.

By this time, it was bedtime. We brushed our teeth, washed, and got into our pajamas, but there was no way we were sleepy after all the excitement. We were determined to find that ghost.

My sister stood lookout at the West window for the ghost. My brother began at the East window but quickly reconsidered, abandoned his post and joined my sister instead. I was at the North window. That was in my parents' bedroom.

Their room was over the kitchen and had a stovepipe that came up through the kitchen and continued on through their room. We could lie on our bellies and hear what was going on in the kitchen. I heard my dad come into the house. I heard my mother say, "Floyd, what on earth happened to my sheet?"

I heard my father reply, "God, Audrey! They chased me! I barely made it into the barn!"

My faith in the supernatural was shaken that night.

But I never did tell my sister and brother what I had heard through the stovepipe. I figured little kids needed ghosts to be scared of, especially the night before Hallowe'en.

BROTHER BEAR

'Famous among the barns'

MY SISTER-IN-LAW, Sandy, likes to wear sparkley clothes. She likes getting all dressed up and going out. But my brother is a farmer, most comfortable in Co-op garb. In fact, the only time I'd ever seen him really dressed up was at their wedding.

Sandy and her sister used to drive into the city to Mannequin Sales and Theatre Supplies to buy props, mannequins and decorations for the window displays at their clothing store. They'd go for lunch and then spend the afternoon trying on costumes and giggling a great deal.

That's where Sandy got the idea for the vacation. She had found out that being married to a farmer meant having no money and no time off. For the sun-loving, fun-loving Sandy, this was a fate worse than death.

It was the bear costume that gave her the idea. Then she picked out a circus tuxedo coat, blue and silver, silver tights, a rhinestone top hat, and a little whip.

She wasn't sure Jim would go for the idea but she did all that she could to convince him. He did try on the bear costume she had rented. He was a little shaky on the bicycle but he was a natural at the dancing. The costume seemed to bring out the playful, frisky animal in him.

Sandy made up flyers on the computer at work and got on the phone to everyone she knew. They got jobs — bear gigs — at kids' birthday parties, service club fundraisers, retirement home fun days, fall fairs, community corn roasts and barbeques, and even between periods at the local hockey games. They bought the costumes and were in the bear entertainment business.

Within eight months, they had the money for a one-week vacation and very strange income tax deductions.

But where to go? A cruise? An island resort? NO, not Agribition in Saskatchewan! NO, not the Texas Cattlemen's show! The latter were my brother's first choices, but Sandy did not want to look at the rear end of any cattle beast on her vacation! She wanted sun and sand and drinks with little paper umbrellas in them. A compromise. Two days at the Texas Cattlemen's Show and five days at a Mexican resort. A deal. And, hey, why not take the costumes and make a little extra money while there?

Sandy called the organizers of the Texas Cattlemen's Show and got a bear gig at the Saturday night beef banquet. They called their act, Farmers Will Do Anything for Money, So Bear With Us. They had a great time and made two hundred American dollars to boot. For a Canadian farmer that was serious money!

Perhaps it was the exuberance of that triumph that led them to go too far. Perhaps it was their naivete that got them into trouble.

They were staying in a lovely little Spanish style

hacienda where guitar players serenaded the visitors at the cafes around the square. It was too hot during the day to wear the bear costume, and so they waited until the second evening to add to the entertainment in the square.

The Mexicans are sticklers for paper work, and Jim and Sandy were not prepared for the police who showed up in the middle of the act.

Sandy, you see, had no bear owner's licence, no performer's visa, and no permission form to conduct business in Mexico. She also did not speak any Spanish.

Now, my brother, still in full costume, should not have tried to punch the arresting officer. He was damned lucky the tranquillizer gun was the only weapon they used.

So my sister-in-law spent her vacation in a Mexican jail while Jim was sent back to Texas to a S.P.C.A. holding pen. By the time the Canadian Embassy got Sandy out of that jail, she'd learned quite a bit of Spanish, most of it unrepeatable.

My brother woke up and found himself in a big cage. He was confused, upset and then angry.

He still tells the story of the look on the officer's face when 'the bear' started yelling at him to let him out, and then he cursed the poor man for standing there with his mouth open! That jaw widened more when my brother finally thought to take his head off . . . the bear head that is.

After they finally got home, the local paper did a feature story on their adventures. Then they got a call from The Shirley Show to appear, in costume, and tell their story. Then they got a call from the entertainment people from the C.N.E. and the Royal Winter Fair. When they got the gig at Agribition, Sandy started speaking Spanish again.

BLUEBERRY/RASPBERRY JAM

1 pt. blueberries
1 qt. red raspberries
7 cp. sugar
1 bottle liquid fruit pectin
• Crush berries; measure
  4 c. (if necessary, add water
  to make 4 c.)
• Add sugar, mix well. Heat to
  full rolling boil; boil hard 1
minute, stirring constantly.
Remove from heat; stir in
pectin; skim.
• Ladle into sterilized hot jars
  to within 1/8″ of jar top.
  Wipe jar rim; adjust lids.
  Process in boiling water
  bath 5 minutes.
Makes 10 half pints.

RED RASPBERRY/PLUM JAM

4 lbs. tart red plums,
  pitted (9 c.)
1 c. red raspberries (1 lb.)
sugar
• Grind together plums and
  raspberries. Measure pulp
  and for each cup of pulp,
  add 1 c. sugar. Combine in
  large saucepan. Bring to
boil and boil about 20 minutes, stirring frequently.
• Ladle into sterilized hot jars
  to within 1/8″ of jar top.
  Wipe jar rim; adjust lids.
  Process in boiling water
  bath 5 minutes.
Makes about 5 pints.

MY
GRANDMOTHER'S QUILT

"...that time would take me up to the swallow
thronged loft by the shadow of my hand,"

MY GRANDMOTHER'S MEMORIES were a crazy patch work quilt, the bits and pieces randomly placed and stitched together. I listened wide-eyed to her snatches of recall and watched her lonely existence in her silent, little rooms. Her giant quilt rack was up all winter. She made a quilt for each granddaughter, seven winters of quilting by herself. Those were the times when she talked and I listened.

She would start with a particular pattern or feathers or ice or the pond. The pond story was my favourite because, at four years old, my father was the hero. He ran to the house to get gramma to save his baby sister who was floating face down in the water. My grandmother ran from the house, waded into the cold water, and saw the little white dress under the water. She caught the fabric, and pulled the little girl out in time. Little Mae was saved that day because of my father's presence of mind, and my grandmother's determination not to lose another child.

Feathers would start the stories about her job at the millinery, making hats for the rich people of Port Huron. The chemicals and smell in the carding rooms made her ill, and so she worked with the colourful feathers, putting the speckled pheasant feathers on men's hat bands and sweeping, elegant feathers on fancy ladies' hats. She had her own money and her own room then. Her voice told me how proud she was of her independence.

Ice reminded her of the death of her mother. My great-grandmother had been on her way home after sitting up all night with a sick neighbour. She took a short-cut across a frozen stream and fell through the ice near the shore. Over the next few days, she developed blood-spitting pneumonia and, at age thirty-three, died leaving my grandmother to take her place. Gramma at age ten was the oldest girl in a family of eight children. This meant no more school. It meant cooking, cleaning, and minding the little ones. A big job for a little girl.

Her father remarried two years later to a woman who did not wish to share the household with so many children. Gramma was hired out to two elderly women in town. For three years she cared for them. She taught me a few phrases in Gaelic that she'd learned there.

She told me about the time she came to a dance in Appin where a young man patted the seat next to him to invite her to sit by him. He told her that she was pretty. From the pictures of her youth, I think he was right. She was fair-skinned, dark-haired, and petite.

At that point, a cloud would fall on her memories. When I asked questions, she would invite me to look at old, musty books, play with the fancy buttons in the green glass button box or eat biscuits with strawberry jam.

Years later, I dug out some of the pieces of her life myself. Gramma had married Leonard and moved to his farm. They had had twins who died soon after birth. Then she had another child who also died. Baby ghosts haunted her memories.

Then my uncle was born, followed by my father and my aunt. Three lived. Then she had Marie who was a blonde angel my grandmother loved dearly. The effort and expense of a city doctor did not save her; Marie died when she was sixteen months old. A light seemed to go out in my grandmother's life then. Seven children born and three left alive. No wonder clouds covered those memories.

She never spoke of my grandfather to me. I found out that at fifty-two he took his own life, leaving gramma and my teenaged aunt to find him. It was World War II and my father was in the army still stationed in Canada. My father left the army, hitch-hiked home to bury his father, and took over the work of the farm. My gramma had her own part of the house where I was raised.

When the quilt rack filled her living room and part of the dining room, I'd say, "Gramma, it's so big. You'll never get all this done."

She'd reply, "Yes, I will. You watch. You just have to keep at it everyday."

In the end, she gave me a patchwork of her uneven memories from the fabric of her grief-filled life, and a daisy quilt, a Dresden Plate, made from sugar bags, flour sacks, housedresses, aprons, tablecloths, pillowcases, and thousands of tiny, even stitches.

She also gave me the lesson that you just have to keep at it every day.

DRESDEN PLATE QUILT PATTERN

THE LAST CHANCE
BONEYARD DANCE
DEAD AHEAD

"Time held me green and dying"

WHEN GARY GOT THE JOB with the old folks over at the Manor, his employers told him three things: keep them busy, keep them happy, and keep them safe. He did just that. He got lawn bowling tournaments going, organized birthday bashes, and set up the pen pal club, and cribbage club through the local public school. He also started the 10k walking club that walked every day unless it rained or got too cold or windy or hot.

Pretty soon most of the residents remembered his name and looked forward to seeing him come along in his jeans and runners. They liked his enthusiasm and energy. He put up a suggestion box that folks actually used. That's how they got the little garden going out back, the pet visiting day every week, and the occasional baseball or hockey game outing. The Manor was turning into a happening place, Gary told his friends.

It was his idea for the weekly dances and fishing trips his first summer there. Some of his friends would come over and jam and play requests, or "Stump the Young Folks", as Jimmy, the spoon player, called the Friday dance. Old Clarence brought out his fiddle and Arthur would chord on the piano. Elsie would sing My Sweet Little Alice Blue Gown or My Grandfather's Clock. Hector would get danced off his feet as he was the best and often only dancer among the male residents. Bess danced every dance, partner or not.

As for the fishing trips, those same six people always signed up for the Saturday outing. The van held eight people, so Gary would drive those six and his girlfriend, Roberta, whose job it was to keep everyone focused on fishing rather than wandering off into the wilderness. Clarence, the fiddler, Arthur, the piano man, Hector, the dancer, Jimmy, the spoon player, and Elsie and Bess, the cheerleaders of the group, all looked forward to that day away from the routine of the residence.

Keeping everyone with a baited, unsnagged pole was Gary's job while keeping everyone in sight was Roberta's. The one who really made that a challenge was Hector who was eighty-two years young, 6'5" tall, and prone to go a long way off to answer the call of nature.

Old Clarence, the Don Messer of the group, had the best luck actually catching fish. He had had his own country dance band from the time of Glenn Miller through the Beatles to Michael Jackson, though none of those notables actually influenced his music. Elsie Watson signed up for anything that Gary was involved with because she thought he was the cutest thing since Robert Goulet, and he brought a sense of fun into the Boneyard, as she dubbed the Manor. Bess Mathews just wanted to be where the action was. Hector, Arthur, and Jimmy appreciated the chance to get out of doors, enjoy some fresh air, and tell lies about past fishing adventures. They also seemed to take great pleasure in peeing in the bushes once again.

They came home for Saturday supper worn out and happy. Roberta pointed out to Gary that she was just worn out, and did not want to have to hunt up Hector from one of his jaunts afield ever again! She, for one, was glad the season was over and ice fishing was definitely out with this crew.

Gary was doing just fine at his job until he decided to take those six residents to the Grateful Dead concert in Hamilton the following March. He should have known better. Roberta often pointed that out to him.

The friends he had been planning to go with had flipped their van the day before the concert causing concussions, contusions, and ticket confusions. Gary therefore had six extra tickets and no way to get to Hamilton. It just seemed logical to him to bring six of the music fans from The Manor, use the van, and pay for the tickets from the social convenor's budget. It was perfect! He'd get to go, recover his costs, and still have friends who liked to dance in the adjoining seats. Roberta was not so optimistic!

Everybody got all dressed up to go to the concert. Hector wore his best and only suit. He said that the excitement of the occasion reminded him of a CKNX Saturday Night Barn Dance! Gary heaved a sigh of relief when they made it through all the Deadheads in the parking lot and found their seats. Then the house lights went down, the Grateful Dead took the stage, and the sweet sound of Jerry Garcia's guitar sent the audience wild with Mississippi Half-Step, Toodle-doo.

Elsie had a whale of a time step dancing with every Deadhead who would dance with her. Clarence played an air fiddle and rolled back the years to the days of his youth. Jimmy smiled along with the stoned smokers behind them, and nodded his head to the music all night. Bess showed some pretty spaced out twirlers a few Charleston steps that they incorporated into their dervish dance. Arthur broke down and got out his pocketbook during intermission, bought a tie-dye T-shirt and wore it under his suit coat.

It probably would have worked out just fine if Hector

hadn't drunk all that Gatorade and gone a long way off to answer the call of nature. By the time Roberta realized he was missing, it was the middle of the second set and Gary was having such a good time that she didn't want to worry him. After all, it shouldn't be too hard to find a 6'5", eighty-two-year-old in his best brown suit in a crowd of Deadheads.

She started with the washrooms. At first she asked young men to look for him inside, but they did not seem to take her very seriously. One fellow asked if she was looking for a rabbit named Harvey. Another one suggested she was a spaced out chick who should go to the Rock Med room. After that she went straight into the men's washrooms calling, "Hector, Hector, where are you?"

She got replies like, "Hector's not here, man."

Next, she tried asking security if they had seen a 6'5", eighty-two year old and met with some very blank stares. They seemed a bit overwhelmed by what they had seen already that night. She tried walking around the perimeter, but it was the last encore by then and the excitement was running pretty high. In fact, pretty high was a good general description of both the atmosphere and the audience.

Roberta finally returned to their seats, harried and Hectorless. Gary had been concerned and, now that everyone was leaving, a bit scared. The last song had been *"Knock, Knock, Knockin' on Heaven's Door,"* and Gary hoped that Hector wasn't. The next few minutes were tearful, anxious, and very long. They searched everywhere they were allowed to go. Security people helped as best they could. The police were called. Finally, a missing person's report was filed. The van returned very late to The Manor minus one tall passenger.

Gary's job was on the line. Hector's family threatened to sue. When they found that he'd gone missing at a Grateful Dead concert, they got downright nasty.

Two long desperate days later, a call came from Albany, New York, from the newest roadie for the Grateful Dead. Hector was on tour! He would not be back until early April when the tour ended in Atlanta. Gary was sent down to bring him back, but he had some holiday time coming. As it turned out, they didn't get back until early April, just in time for the opening of the fishing season.

Roberta had no trouble finding them that year. They all wore their tie-dyes fishing!

SHUT UP AND FISH

*"And once below a time I lordly
had the trees and leaves*

Trail with daisies and barley

Down the rivers of the windfall light."

TERRY WAS ABOUT FOUR WHEN HIS FATHER, Bill, first took him fishing. Bill and Jill's second daughter had just been born and father and son both just wanted to get away.

They went down along the river that skirted their small town. They didn't catch much, a carp, a few little bass, a catfish once and awhile. It was a good way to get some peace and quiet, acting out a weekend ritual during the fishing season.

They'd go to the market early in the morning to shop for their lunch and then go home and make it. Terry once asked why Mom didn't make their lunch and Bill asked, "Who's goin' fishin'?"

"Us."

"Who's eatin' the lunch?"

"Us."

"Then, who's makin' the lunch?"

"Us."

"Right you are!"

That was the simple logic that Bill lived by and Terry could not argue with that.

Bill always got the same stuff for his lunch: garlic dill pickles from the Hungarian lady, salami, rye bread, sardines from the Greek guy, hunks of cheese and some fruit, and then he made a super sweet thermos of coffee to wash it down. Terry got whatever he felt like that day but it always included cookies from the bakery stall. He had to take his own drink because Bill said that coffee would stunt his growth and would not allow him even a sip.

They'd pack up the truck that said BILL'S AUTOBODY on the side with an umbrella, a ground sheet, rods, reels, tackle box, cooler, thermos, rain gear, boots, knife, a stringer, landing net — and extra dry socks: they'd had more than their fair share of soakers. They'd be gone by nine and fishing by nine thirty.

Bill never was a man to say too much but he did teach Terry quite a bit about fishing. How a good fisherman listens, how he can hear the big one jump up stream, how he can hear the big one thinking. How a good fisherman watches for snags, whirlpools, branches, weather, water bugs, and currents. A good fisherman pays attention to what he is doing.

"You have to be smarter than the fish," he was fond of saying.

For about six years, they fished that river, explored her banks and currents, found the good spots, caught what there was to catch, got soakers, landed a few big ones, got to know each other better, shared ritual lunch making and eating, along with an appreciation for nature, quiet, fishing skills, and each other's company.

When Terry turned 10, Bill was as excited as a kid at Christmas. He was getting him a very special birthday present — a boat. Nothing fancy. Just a little aluminum job with a five horse motor. But this would open up a whole new world of fishing possibilities. Big rivers and maybe even lakes. Much greater chance to catch big ones.

Terry was as excited as Bill, and they got out a map from Fisheries Canada and began to plan their weekends.

Jill was happy enough to see them go. Bill worked really hard at the shop and he seemed to come back rested and refreshed from fishing. It kept Terry out from under her feet and let her get the shopping and the laundry done and spend some time with her daughters who took no interest in fishing. Shopping was more to their liking, or going to the library or a movie. It all worked out pretty well.

Bill and Terry found a couple of lakes they would head out to on a Saturday. This time they'd take the camping gear and not get back until Sunday afternoon. They didn't go every weekend, but often enough to maintain their self-images as fishermen. They spent hours in that boat with very few words between them, just a gentle companionship and understanding of what it took to fish, to land the big one.

The year Terry was going to be sixteen, they were all

packed and ready for the opening weekend of the season. That Friday, Terry was going to his first high school dance. Bill drove him there in the truck and said he'd be back around eleven.

He was. Right on time as usual. But it was a police officer who met him at the school and asked if he was Terry's father. Bill said that he was and the officer invited him to come into the principal's office for a few minutes. Terry was there with four of his buddies, and the vice-principal was there, too.

The vice-principal explained to Bill that Terry would be suspended for five days, charged with drinking under age, and would have to appear in court the next week. She explained that the boys had purchased bottles of beer from one of the seniors who was selling them for $3.00 a bottle from the trunk of his car in the school parking lot, and that she had already phoned Jill. She waited for Bill to say something but he didn't. She said that he could take Terry home now. They both got up and left without looking at each other, nor at anyone else for that matter.

When they got home, Jill was on the warpath like neither of them had ever seen her! Terry was going to be grounded until he was twenty-one, pay any fine he got through the courts himself, and go to AA meetings forever, if that was what it took!

Terry was swallowing hard and often. He just about teared over when she said that was it for his fishing career, too. It was then that Bill spoke up. "We'll be goin' fishin' first thing in the morning."

"You most certainly will not!" was what she started to say, but after seeing the stubborn set of Bill's jaw, settled for, "We'll see about that!"

Jill was mortified. What would people think? What could the boy have been thinking? What would be next if they didn't clamp down and clamp down hard? What message were his sisters going to get if Terry was allowed away with this kind of stunt?

Bill motioned Terry to get up to bed.

Jill protested, "You can't go fishing tomorrow. That's rewarding him. That's ignoring what has just happened. Aren't you taking this seriously at all?"

"Yup. I am. That's why we're going fishing."

That was the end of that.

They drove up to the lake in an uncomfortable silence, launched the boat, picked their spot, anchored, and got the lines in the water.

In about a half an hour, Terry began to justify his actions.

In a very offhand manner, he said, "Everybody does it, dad. One beer. What's the harm? No big deal." He was fishing all right, testing the waters.

His father just turned and looked at him, took his measure, seriously and slowly. He turned back to the water and, in a voice edged with contempt, said, "Shut up and fish."

After a few more tense minutes passed he heard the sniffles, and then a sob. Bill turned to look at his son. Terry whispered, "I'm sorry, dad." Then his shoulders began to heave.

Bill waited a full minute, and then handed over a cotton handkerchief. He waited for a few good honks before he offered to take the day off work to go to court with his son.

"I'll come this time, boy, but never again. This is the only time I'm doin' that on your account."

"There won't be another time, dad."

"You better tell that to your mother. I've never seen her so worked up."

Bill unscrewed the thermos of coffee, poured a steaming cup, and offered it to Terry.

"Here. Warm up your innards."

"Aren't you afraid it will stunt my growth, dad?"

Terry's voice was a little brighter now.

"Nope. You seem to be growin' pretty good." Bill poured the boy another cup of coffee. "Now, let's catch a big one."

And they did.

Ten years later, Terry had married Carolyn and they had a little William who made a racket every night for a month after he came home from the hospital.

Bill and Jill came up to the city for a weekend to meet their new grandson. Over a late breakfast, Bill suggested to the bleary-eyed Terry, "You're going to have to teach that boy to fish, and soon."

"Yeah. I was counting on some help from you, Dad."

"Sure," said Bill. "It takes a while to make a good fisherman like you or me. I'll have a talk with that little fella tonight. See if we can't get started."

"Thanks, Dad. We could sure use a break and some sleep."

Little William took a couple of nights of hearing about the fundamentals of fishing before he calmed down into a sleep-all-night routine. His grandfather figured he had great potential as a fisherman.

BUSTED!

"I ran my heedless ways"

I WAS LEANING OVER to get a King Crimson record when the sliding door at the back of the suburban townhouse cracked open and a gun was in my face. It had bullets. I could see them. The hair on the back of my neck stood on end as I stared into the small, dark hole inches from my face.

It was 1970 and I was 21 years old. I was at a party with friends from high school days who were then at university. The man with the gun sat me down on a cushioned stool and ran into the kitchen shouting. I was numb with shock. I could hear crashing and yelling. It was a chaotic blur.

I do remember the thirteen of us being hustled into two paddy wagons with barred windows, the five girls in one and the seven guys in another. I was in my first year of teaching high school. My principal would not understand. My parents would be devastated!

The revolution we had wanted to be a part of had settled harmlessly into loud music, too much alcohol and dope, a few posters of Che Guevera and Karl Marx, and sharing stories from demonstrations gone by. I was not sure which of these was the reason we were on our way to jail.

One woman was from Germany, married to a Canadian; two were American sisters, one married to a Canadian; their husbands were brothers, nephews to the local judge. Another guy was the minister's son from our small town, another a doctor's daughter, and I was a farmer's daughter in my first few weeks of teaching. We were all very scared and shaken.

Lock up. Dank, smelly, a toilet with no lid or rim. Good guy cop with cigarettes. A big, noisy, bad guy with threats of deportation and jail time for our heinous crimes against the state. These crimes apparently included possession of marijuana, and possession for the purpose of trafficking, and possession of dangerous weapons. Someone had brought in a school pack filled with grass, and they had found a switchblade knife someone had brought back from Europe, and a machete someone else had brought from a trip to Mexico.

We were questioned separately.

"We just want to know who the stuff belongs to —" from the gentle good guy cop offering a cigarette.

"I don't smoke and I don't know."

"Come on. You're a smart girl. You don't have to go down with these scum. Your whole future is at stake here."

"I don't know really. It was a party. People came and went."

"Did you notice a backpack in the kitchen?"

"No."

"Did you know about the stuff in the basement?"

"I wasn't in the basement."

"Were you so stoned you didn't know what was going on?"

"I was playing music and talking with my friends in the living room. Sometimes we danced. I was getting tired."

"Do you want to write your story into a statement? You don't seem like the rest."

He said this to everyone we found out when we compared notes back in the cell. Divide and conquer. Isolate. Generate mistrust, desperation, and fear.

A long, scary night. No sleep. No food or water. A full view of the users of the rimless toilet. Joined by a drunken woman later.

Fingerprints. Front view. Side view.

Transfer to county lock up. Clothes taken. Showers with no privacy. Blue outfits.

Clothes back. To court. Uncle judge on the bench. Bail set.

Sunday afternoon we are sprung. Out! Free! Meet with the lawyer as a group soon. Have to teach tomorrow.

We found out that we would need lots of money. I called Mom. She saw the article in the paper. She said we sounded like dangerous mobsters instead of the kids from town. She and Dad were pretty upset She cashed the insurance policy that was going to help pay for my student loan.

I was angry and ashamed at the same time, afraid the people at the school would find out and fire me as unfit to teach their children, that my family would be grist for the small town rumour mill.

We met with the lawyer — corduroy, pipe, calm reassurances, lectures about the Criminal Code, court procedure, strategies. We went to court the next week. Some plead guilty; some did not. Charges were added while others were dropped.

Months went by. Appearances, delays, days off work, meetings with lawyers.

The last time, the day of the trials, I was scared. We all marched in and took our places. It reminded me of church, the judge in the pulpit. My girlfriend elbowed my ribs and nodded toward the back of the court. I turned and saw my father sitting in his Sunday suit. He was hunched forward and turning his good hat around and around in his rough hands. He did not look up. He sat there silent and stoic. He was the only parent to come. A lump came into my throat and didn't go away.

I really was not paying attention until the lawyer started shaking my hand. My girlfriends were laughing and crying. The charges had been dropped against all the females. When I turned around, my dad was gone.

We never talked about that day. I wish I had said, "It was very brave and decent of you to come." or "Thank you for being there, Dad. It meant a lot to me."

A Visit To Gramma's

*"About the lilting house
and happy as the grass was green,"*

ONCE UPON A TIME, there was a gramma, a mother, and a girl. One summer, the mother said that the girl was old enough to visit her gramma for a week. At first, the girl was thrilled — a sleep-over for a whole week! Then she began to wonder what they would do. She could only play so much cribbage or checkers.

Gramma lived way out in the middle of nowhere with no malls, no video stores, not even close neighbours. Gramma had no T.V., no VCR, no dishwasher! She didn't even know who the Simpsons were!

As the mother and the girl drove to gramma's, the girl asked her mother when she would be coming back to get her. She made her mother promise not to be late, and to call her at least once in case she had to come and take her home early.

They drove off the main highway onto a gravel road until they came to gramma's cabin surrounded by her gardens. The small, white cottage was in the middle of a green meadow with woods at the back. Gramma was standing on the porch waiting with lemonade and oatmeal cookies.

The girl hugged her mother very tight when she left to go back to the city and tried hard not to cry.

Gramma showed her all around the gardens so that she could find the raspberries, the peas, the butterflies, the little cucumbers, all the salad ingredients and the herbs like basil and parsley. Then they picked some flowers for the bowl on the kitchen table and gramma asked if she would like some flowers for her room up in the loft. Then they picked some wild flowers from the garden out back.

The girl loved her bed up in the eaves of the cabin. It didn't have a door and she had to climb a ladder to take her bag up there. It was so cozy with one of gramma's quilts and two fat pillows with embroidered flowered cases. It smelled like clean cotton sheets and wildflowers. A round window looked out on the wildflower garden and the trees. She could stand up tall only in the very middle. It was a great bedroom for a girl!

That afternoon they baked biscuits, drank tea from china cups, picked berries, gathered salad stuff and talked about when the mother had been a girl. They made a simple supper of salad, ham and cheese sandwiches, followed by real cream with the berries and biscuits. After they did the dishes together, gramma showed her how to embroider flowers for her pillow cases at home. She had piles of lovely colours of yarn. The girl used as many as possible and was tying knots and threading needles for hours. It was fun!

That night it rained and the sound of the rain on the roof was so soothing that she fell right asleep. The next morning everything smelled so fresh and looked so green. It was still damp outside and so they made raspberry squares, blueberry buckle, and jam right from scratch. Two kinds!

After lunch and lip smacking pan licking, they went for a walk to the neighbour's to trade jam for cream, butter, and eggs. They found a turtle and two frogs in the ditch on the way there, and saw a blue heron on the way back. After supper, they looked at old photographs and gramma told stories about all the people and places in the pictures. The girl found a picture of her mother with pigtails and great big teeth. She looked really funny!

The next day was spent working in the garden, digging little drainage ditches and cutting the little front lawn. The girl was exhausted that night and went right to bed after a supper of cold chicken, potato salad, and carrot salad and, for dessert, raspberry squares and tea.

The third day, they painted part of the porch and two planters. Then they went for a walk by the edge of the woods and found birds' nests, fuzzy worms and a garter snake. Gramma wasn't even scared! Later, they went out on the front lawn with a blanket, stretched out on it and played a game called, "What do the clouds look like?" That night they sat on the porch and listened for frogs, owls, and crickets and watched the batty bats doing their amazing air-o-bat-ics.

The fourth day they sat on the porch with lemonade and sugar cookies and finally played crib for a penny a point. They saw lots of butterflies that day and retold stories they both had told many times before.

A lady came to visit and brought packages of meat wrapped in pink paper, and gramma gave her the baby quilt she had made for her new baby. That night they talked about babies. It wasn't so weird as when her mother talked about that kind of thing.

The fifth day it rained again, so they baked peach pies and a pound cake. She finished the pillowcases she had started already. Gramma braided her hair as she used to with the girl's mother. Then gramma showed her a scrap-book that her mother had made when she was in public school about somebody named 'Trudeau'. It was really good!

The last whole day, gramma took her on a walk right into the woods, down a well worn path into the middle of the grove. They stopped in a little clearing and gramma put down a blanket and the picnic basket.

She pointed to the path that they had come down and said that it was the path of Love, and then she pointed to another path to their right and said that it was the path of Beauty. The path behind them was the path of Truth and the path in front of them was the path of Wisdom. She said that after lunch, the girl could choose which path she was going to walk.

The girl was a little confused and asked what this was all about. Gramma explained that a girl needs a way to know how to make up her mind about things in life and these four paths would help her do that. The path of Love meant she was to listen to her heart and follow whom and whatever she loved. If she chose the path of Beauty, she would create and preserve whatever she found beautiful. The path of Truth meant telling and serving the cause of Truth.

When the girl asked about the path of Wisdom, gramma said that it was the other three put together and that when the girl got older like her gramma, she would probably choose the path of Wisdom. She said that each path would go to a clearing and that not following a path would mean getting lost in the woods. The girl said that she thought she understood and they had their picnic.

When her mother came the next day, they had iced tea and pie on the porch. Gramma gave them a whole peach pie to take home, packed the embroidered pillowcases, gave the girl a big hug and asked if she would like to come back next year. The girl said she couldn't wait.

On the way back in the car, the girl asked her mother which path she was on. The mother said they were on the 401. The girl said that she meant Love, Beauty, Truth or Wisdom. Her mother's thoughts flew back to another picnic in that woods years ago. Then she and the girl had a talk like they never had before!

The next year, the girl went to her grandmother's place for one week and then the mother went there for a week too. They both learned more about the richness of life, the choices they had and more about Love, Beauty, Truth and Wisdom.

The
Saskatchewan
Suite

W HEN I CAME TO THE PRAIRIES, the big sky, the long summer days, the cowboy boots, the pickup trucks with guns across the back windows, the old cabin, the interesting array of neighbours, the bright yellow fields of canola and sunflowers against an azure blue sky, the Western movie little towns, the ever-present prairie dogs, the long, flat distances, and the haunting coyote cries made quite an impression on me. Reading *WHO HAS SEEN THE WIND* had only partially prepared me.

W. O. Mitchell would have appreciated the humour of the Eastener plunked into the farming community one hundred miles north of Yorkton. I was so busy surviving, chasing one animal or another, cutting wood, hauling water and feed, cooking on the wood stove, and figuring out the neighbourhood politics, I barely had time to write letters home. The incredible people I met, the pioneer history I learned, and the vivid memories of that time inspired these stories.

Taken from the book,
REFLECTIONS from the KELLIHER JASMIN DISTRICT
published by the Kelliher Historical Society,1982

THE KELLIHER CO-OPERATIVE WOMEN'S GUILD
*The purpose of the Saskatchewan Women's Guild
is to give leadership in the Co-op movement.*

OUR CREED
*For ourselves-freedom and growth of character.
For our children-a higher social order, economic opportunities and security.
For the world-peace among nations and a common goal
— the welfare of mankind.*

THE SASKATCHEWAN WHEAT POOL
*The organizing of the Saskatchewan Wheat Pool, of which Kelliher Pool forms a
part, was only a continuation of the struggle by the farming industry for a
better deal. A complete history of the struggle would fill a book and extend back
more than a century. Wheat was grown in the Red River Valley in 1813 by a
few settlers brought out by Lord Selkirk,.......{Fur traders} believed that if the
farming industry was allowed to expand it would be the end of the fur trade.
They used every means at their disposal to make it fail, even burning their
buildings, killing their stock and even some of the settlers themselves,
but the settlement still survived.*

THE LUBENOW FAMILY
*My dad got a homestead of 160 acres, that was a quarter of land for ten dollars
which he broke with a team of oxen and a hand plough with the lines around his
neck so he could hang on to the handles of the plough. He would say, "Haw"
and "Gee" and the oxen would know their directions.*

*The first thing he did was make a place to live in for shelter.
He dug out a hill and then fixed it with poles so it wouldn't cave in, that is
what you would call a hovel. We lived in that hovel until he built a log house,
where they raised 12 children.*

*My mom did a lot of things too, such as making quilts with washed sheep's wool
and dyed flour bags. These she tied with coloured yarn. My dad carded the
wool for quilting. Mom also milked cows and set the incubator with 100 eggs
for chickens. She also lathed the log house inside, then the wall was ready for
plastering with a mixture of clay, water and straw chaff.
She used a trowel to make a smooth job. Then she brushed white
wash on the wall mixed with a little blueing to make a nice white.*

One of our most pleasurable times occurred at the dances...when we went as a family, or the Christmas cancerts-babies bundled up in blankets and put to bed on the top of the school desks, while the parents and the older children enjoyed themselves and then looked forward to the ride home in the open sleigh or closed in cutter.

True pioneers they were; they came to virgin land where many artifacts reminded them of the first population of the area. Buffalo bones and skulls were on the corner of the quarter section and several Indian stone hammerheads were found in the yard. These hammerheads served as doorstops for many years. On the way to the country school were two Indian graves, and a half a mile east of the Campbell place, a buffalo rubbing stone.

When they got to their homestead, it was nothing but wild prairire, bush and sloughs The first thing they had to do was build a sod shack, and while doing it had no shelter from the weather.

They lived in a mud hut for a number of years.

"These pioneers came from the United States, Scotland, England, Ukraine, Sweden, Hungary, Russia, Poland, Germany, Ireland, France, Wales, Norway and many came on the C.P.R. and some worked for the railway for a time too."

The teacher's salary was $65.00 per month and $4.00 a month for janitor work.

Antoine Hamelin was married to Philomin Perrault. Antoine was a buffalo hunter and trader. He used to Leave Fort Garry in the early spring fully loaded with staples of the day, which he bartered for buffalo hides. On these trips they lived mostly on pemmican and jerky. He had up to forty red river carts. These camps had to be of considerable size, big enough to be able to repel any attack from the warring Indian tribes.

His first wife was known as Madame Cariou and she was the first woman I ever saw smoking, it was pretty rare in those days, 1922. He told of early experiences, when he walked to Fort Qu'Appelle for supplies. He told of bringing a bottle of whiskey back one time along with other supplies. This trip the snow was very deep, so he just kept throwing the bottle of whiskey as far as he could, would walk to it, pick it up and throw it again.

My recollection of one particularly memorable time was about 1937, on the eve of the concert when my father harnesses the horses with addition of brass sleigh bells placed on the neck harness. The sleight was pre-warmed with charcoal foot-warmers, and we all sat around the sleigh box covered with blankets for the two mile trip to the schoolhouse.

All the farmers worked together to get the harvest in while the weather was good, so this period lasted for three to four weeks. I recall the great excitemant of taking lunches out to the threshing outfit as well as all the hustle and bustle at meal time around the table. The huge roasts, fresh baked bread, garden vegetables, pies must have taken hours to prepare by my mother and older sisters.

THE SNIPE

It was late in June
and the heat of high noon
found the boys in the coffee shop
way out of Wild Rose Country
where the hot wind never stops.

There was Bill and Cliff
from over near Skiff
and Ern from Foremost you see
and a few other guys but I don't know their name
for Ern was the boss to me.

Well I'd come to the west and I'd been blessed
I found a job about a week ago
on a dry land farm – 20 miles from town
so different from Ontario

Now I was only 18 and very naive
a newcomer fresh from the East
and I was doing my best to fit in with the rest
cause I was young and eager to please.

And Ern said, "Boys I think it's time
to go out late at night
with a burlap bag and a big flashlight
and we'll try to catch a snipe!"

So if you've a chance to come to my ranch
and join us on a drive
We'll let this newcomer flush them out
and we'll catch a snipe alive.

Then everyone nodded and shook his head
with winks that I couldn't see
and they all figured out a kind of a plan
and explained it carefully to me.

There's a deep water hole just over the knoll
around here folks call it a slew
and the snipes gather in the cool dark air
if you see one here's what to do.

Shine the light in his eyes and put him right in the bag
you can catch him he'll do you no harm
but if he runs astray just drive him our way
we'll be waiting for you at the barn.

Well it sounded so easy how could I go wrong
and I sure didn't want to seem dumb
and I sure didn't dare mention that I'd never heard tell
of a snipe where I came from.

And I didn't know it was all a big gag
there was no such animal to be found
I didn't realize they were pulling my leg
and they were just fooling around.

So late that night by the moon's pale light
I packed all my gear on my back
set out for the slew cause I knew what to do
I was gonna put a snipe in the sack.

And I sat in the dark on a hard old rock
and the only sounds thru the hill
were mournful notes of a howling coyote
and it made my blood start to chill.

I sat for hours alone on that slab of stone
waiting for a snipe to show
then I started to ponder, "Now isn't it a wonder
I never heard of this animal before?"

Now did you ever get a deep – gut feeling
that something is just not tight
and you can't make sense of what's going on
no matter how hard you try.

Well that was exactly the way I felt
As I sat there on that stone
with a nagging doubt that I couldn't shut out
and it just wouldn't leave me alone.

And my mind traced over the day's events
and all the things that I'd heard said
and my suspicion grew and I suddenly knew
and my face turned a little bit red.

Then aha said I and I slapped my thigh
I'm amazed at how dumb I can be
that bunch of clowns were just fooling around
and the one they were fooling was me.

So I sat on the rock and I thought and I thought
till I finally came up with a scheme
that would make those guys sorry they even tried
to tease this kid from the East.

Then I snuck to the barn at the front of the farm
where everyone was supposed to be
and sure enough I'd been right
there was no one in sight
just a big black tom cat and me.

I found a can of white paint
that dried real fast
and in just a very short while
I'd pained two stripes from his head to his tail
and I told the cat with a smile
"Now both me and you have a job to do
and I swear you look real enough
Pepe le Peu would be proud of you
and I need you to strut your stuff".

Then we drove into town to the coffee shop
parked the truck way round in the back
and I walked in the door just as big as life
with the animal deep in the sack.

Well the noise died down and there wasn't a sound
as I put the bag at my feet
I took plenty of time cause the audience was mine
and I slowly untied the string.

"Guess you must have gotten tired waiting"
said I as the knot undone,
"Well I'm not sure what a snipe looks like
but I think that I caught us one".

Then the cat crawled out with his new striped coat
just as cool and as proud as could be
and he arched his back and he raised his tail
so that every one could see.

There were cries of surprise and wide open eyes
when they saw what was on the floor
there were chairs in the air and people everywhere
as they scrambled for the door.

And they held their noses and they held their breath
cause the only thing they could see
was the two white stripes on the black cat's back
as they left so hurriedly.

They emptied that place in a second or three
I never knew they could move so fast
my scheme had worked way beyond belief
and I was the last to laugh.

Now that seems such a long time ago
way out on that prairie range
and years have come and years have gone
but some things never change.

Cause it's late in June
and the heat of high noon
found us back in that same coffee shop
way out in Wild Rose Country
where the hot wind never stops.

And there's Bill and Cliff from over near Skiff
and Ern from Foremost you see
and a newcomer here right fresh from the East
and I'm the boss he's eager to please
"Now boys," say I, "I think it's time
to go out late at night
with a burlap bag and a big flashlight
and try to catch a snipe!"

Doug Hollingsworth

GETTING GASSED IN SASKATCHEWAN

"Golden in the heydays of his eyes,"

I'D BEEN INHALING NITROUS OXIDE for two solid hours and I'd felt no pain through the whole dental excavation exercise. When I got out of the dentist's chair, I had tears running down my face, I was weak, and my sides ached from all the laughing. They don't call it laughing gas for nothing!

Then my car decided to play a little trick on me. It had disappeared in the big, snowy parking lot. I'd left my Volkswagen bug parked by the door and now it was gone! It was hiding, playing hide and seek behind the king cab pickups. It was winning, too, the sneaky little devil!

When I finally walked around to the other side of the building, there was my car, right by the door. The dentist must get a real kick out of gassing patients, sending them out a different door, and watching them stumble around the parking lot looking for their vehicle. I could appreciate the joke. I laughed all the way out of Saskatoon.

I turned on CBC radio and it was so witty, so droll, so clever that I laughed uncontrollably. The CBC had never been so funny! The whole landscape was like a giant cartoon from the Dudley Doright RCMP officer who followed me for awhile to the game of pickup truck tag. I was winning. No one had caught me yet!

I was heading home to Kelvington. It was getting darker and colder and snowier but that did not dampen my merry mood. Then I noticed that I was low on fuel. Perfect! February, in Saskatchewan, in the middle of nowhere, in the dark, in the only car left on the road, without any fuel. I laughed so hard my vision was blurred by tears and I needed a washroom.

Then, as if by magic in my cartoon world, relief appeared in the snowy distance. Tall lights shone on a tiny gas station at the crossroads ahead. Two wide tracks curved into the service station. I slowed down very carefully, signalled deliberately to no one in particular, and gently turned to follow the tracks.

Have you ever had a moment when the sum total of your philosophy of life is captured, is affirmed, is proven? It is a sweet moment when you experience satori, great insight, a flash of the cosmic. In this case, it was the cosmic comic, the trickster who steered me unerringly to those snowmobile tracks.

I appreciated the humour again as the car slowly sank to the tops of the windows in the welcoming snow. I began to giggle and then to shriek with laughter.

At this rate, I thought, I was not going to make it to

the pumps, or, more crucially now, to the washroom. Two dark heads peered over the pyramid of 10W30 cans in the window of the station. I turned off the key and the lights, rolled down my window, and crawled out on my belly into the snow.

When I attempted to stand, I plunged waist deep into the soft snow. I floundered around for awhile giving myself a good snow bath. I had the giggles the whole time. It was worse than bedtime giggles with my sister, worse than school girl giggles in the back of the high school library.

Getting to the bathroom on time was no longer an issue. Like Canadian lakes, Canadian snow is warm, once you get in. I swam out on my belly, flailing wildly until I could feel pavement under me. Finally, I stood on unsteady legs and lurched to the entrance, soaked and still laughing hysterically.

The two old timers inside were patient and curious but non-judgmental. They looked like the pair in American Gothic, minus the pitchfork. I finally caught my breath, sobered enough to splutter, "I need gas."

This was followed by a howl of laughter — my own. After all, I'd had a snoot full of gas already!

They looked at each other. They looked at my car or the roof that was showing. They looked at me leaning against the wall for support.

"Yer car's in the ditch," one said flatly.

"I followed the tracks," I protested foolishly.

"Them 're snowmobile tracks."

Another round of side-grabbing snorting on my part.

"We could winch'er," was the suggestion.

"Winch'er. Winch'er Wonderland!" I thought I was so witty that I could be on CBC!

Just then Fate lent a forgiving hand in the form of great Canadian heroes. A bus full of teenage hockey players pulled in. A bunch of them went to my car and literally lifted it out of the snow. It was a Herculean miracle, a

Mighty Mouse cartoon come true!

I mustered some semblance of dignity, or made my best effort, and thanked them profusely. I bought six dollars worth of gas from the two chin scratching old-timers, and they waved as I went on my way, gassed and still giggling.

THE GREAT SHIT LAKE CANOE RACE

"...like a wanderer white

With the dew, come back, the cock on his shoulder:"

I F YOU'VE LIVED IN SASKATCHEWAN, you know what a slough is — a shallow saucer of earth that fills with water in the spring. It is a temporary wetlands area visited by wave after feathered wave of ducks, Canada geese, snow geese and great white swans.

One April, the good people of Kelvington, home of Wendel Clark, decided to have a canoe race on the slough that formed just outside of town. It was known fondly as Shit Lake because that was what the water fowl left behind.

It was $10.00 to enter and quite a few responded. First prize was a trophy and $200.00, a lot of cash just before seeding time. Second prize was a $50.00 gift certificate donated by the Co-op, and third prize was dinner for two at the local hotel, value not to exceed $25.00. The whole community was pretty excited about this event and everyone was happy to get out of doors to meet and greet their neighbours after some very oppressive months of cabin fever.

The race was set for 10:00 a.m. on Saturday, despite the fog, and the pick-ups started bouncing in over the stubbled fields around 9:30. Harvey Melville, the midway judge, headed out for the little island of scrub bushes and trees that was his halfway point station. It was hard to see in the mist, and so he took a shotgun to fire as a signal that the first contestant had made the turn.

The field filled quickly with contestants and spectators. The two fellows from the Co-op were the first on the water warming up, and then two school teachers who brought a screaming entourage of grade 3's and 4's, the vet and his wife, some local farm boys, the Ag. Rep. and some fellow he curled with, the Sweeney twins, two women from the Credit Union, some of the guys from the Nut Mountain Reserve, and some high school students were getting ready to compete. Soon about thirty canoes were juggling for a start position.

It was about three minutes to ten when John and Mickey showed up in the beat-up old half ton, beers in hand, and a canoe in the back. They hustled around and headed down to the water with a straw bale in the centre of the canoe.

"For ballast," said Mickey.

"Need some place to put the beer. Wouldn't want to spill any," joked John. Mickey and John often opened and closed the local hotel. They farmed and sold farm machinery for a few hours in between.

It was cool, overcast and spring-foggy still. People joked about a flock of birds coming in and colliding with the canoes, and about navigation problems in the fog.

"Don't get lost out there! Better take a compass!"

"Watch out fer in-comin' honkers, fellas."

"Don't look up out there. You could get shit-faced! Har, har, har."

"No huntin' allowed. Don't ferget to turn around and come back."

The starter shotgun fired. The first leg of the First Annual Great Shit Lake Canoe Race was off to a fast and furious start. Everyone watched and shouted encouragement until the last canoe was swallowed up by the fog. Then they chatted in groups or wandered back to their vehicles to keep warm.

One group of men began to pass around a mickey of rye "to keep off the chill". A few laid last minute bets while the kids raced up and down the shore discovering treasures. Some of the women gathered around to discuss the births, marriages, and deaths of the last winter.

Then another shotgun report came over the water. Everyone marvelled at the speed of the contestants. The students strained their eyes to be the first to catch sight of the powerful paddlers. Wives and girl friends turned their eyes continually to the water during their conversations. Someone commented on an odd sound, an airplane perhaps. The tension mounted on the shore.

The kids started a commotion at the water's edge. Was it possible? Could stalwart competitors be breaking through the fog so soon?

No question. The dark outline of a canoe and hurried paddlers emerged into the clear water. They were really

moving! Shouts went up. Truck doors slammed as spectators flocked to the shore.

"It's Mickey and John!" came the shocked cry.

Sure enough! The two with the highest odds against
them were finishing first. Spectators exchanged shocked
glances.

A few men waded into the water to land them. The
winners were red faced and puffing. Despite this, they got
help to load the canoe into the old pick-up.

"Let's see the colour of that prize money," said Mickey

"How about a picture for the paper, fellas?"

"Make it quick," quipped John slapping on a silly grin
and hoisting a beer bottle.

"What's yer hurry, boys?"

"We got bets to collect at the hotel and a few rounds
of drinks to buy. Come on in for some free drinks, fellas."

"Here comes another one!" called the kids.

John and Mickey tore out of that field in a real hurry.
A couple of other trucks followed them toward town and
the hotel and the free rounds of drinks.

"There's another one!"

They landed the Ag. Rep and his curling buddy, and
then the two guys from the Co-op and the fellows from
Nut Mountain. They were all talking at once, mostly cuss
words despite the presence of women and children. They
were mad as wet hens. It took a while before they got the
story out about John and Mickey and the outboard motor.

Cheating, thievery, skulduggery, honour and dishon-
our were debated at length. A practical joke, funds for a
few rounds of drinks, threats of beatings, hard feelings,
belly laughs, a load of manure dumped in the back of
Mickey's old half-ton, a few displays of fisticuffs at the
hotel — all of this was repeated and embellished as the stories of the Great Shit Lake Canoe Race travelled the bars,
kitchens, concession roads and telephone lines around that
Saskatchewan town.

Great discussions were held about the ethics of the situation. Men actually came to blows defending or attacking the nervy scoundrels. The outboard motor under that bale of straw made the story last a long time and it was shared with more passion than any honest win ever would have.

Saskatchewan
Hallowe'en

*"As I rode to sleep the owls were
bearing the farm away,"*

WHEN I WAS 25, I moved to Saskatchewan. I was going to take time to write. I got a settler's cabin seven miles outside of a village in return for tutoring a young boy who had had surgery.

It was a rundown, ramshackle shack. No one had lived there for nearly ten years.

I pulled down cobwebs, scrubbed and painted. I drew loads to the dump, hammered and fixed. After a great deal of elbow grease, the kitchen, pantry, bedroom and sitting room were liveable. I blocked off the front bedroom and parlour. There was no running water and so I hauled barrels from town. I got the electricity hooked up again and replaced the glass in some of the windows. I expelled most of the creatures who had taken up residence there.

I worked every other day with the little boy in order not to exhaust him and got another part-time job at the vet clinic in town. It was all going very well, I thought. The neighbours were friendly, always dropping over for tea to see how I was coming along and inviting me back for more tea. Every time I dropped in on anyone, it meant eating a great deal. It also meant storytelling.

I knew far more about the country folk than I ever wanted to, including the two old bachelor brothers who had lived and died in the shack I was now calling home. Mean, nasty, cheap, and bitter they were. Each refused to die because the thought of funeral expenses kept them living. Eventually, they had both died in the house within days of one another and their gaunt bodies were not found for a while. The neighbours all agreed that they were probably still there, still hanging on and refusing to leave their meager property.

This did not bother me, at least not during the day anyway. I was busy getting ready for winter and working in town. The vet had asked if I could board animals that would otherwise be put down. I had warm-heartedly agreed and now was looking after one foundered horse, a weak little cow and her very healthy calf, four goats, a family of kittens, three dogs and four piglets. Looking after them put a big dent into my day!

They got to be my friends, too. I'd take the dogs for runs morning and night, chase the horse and calf when they went on one of their through-the-fence walks, watch the climbing escapades of two kids who liked to climb on my Volkswagen and play King of the Mountain while tap dancing on my paint job. I called them Billy the Kid and Annie Bananie.

Annie always came out to the two-holer with me for company. I'd talk to her and rub her head and teach her not to eat the toilet paper. Annie actually learned to use the outhouse facilities, and so I would allow her to come into the house for a visit sometimes. She liked to explore and was a very good listener.

When I had arrived in Saskatchewan, the daylight lasted until 10:30 p.m. but as fall came the days got shorter. I stacked wood for the wood stove, cleaned the pipes — an awful job —, put plastic on the windows that would sound like a rifle at close range when it was windy, and put rags in cracks and rugs on the floor. I also put a five gallon pail in the basement to avoid going out to the two-holer at night or in bad weather.

It was only in the basement that I was reminded of the two nasty old farmers who had died there. The basement was dark, no electricity there, dirty, and be damned if

I was going to clean it. It was uneven, rocky, and spooky. I avoided going down there if at all possible. I didn't tell anyone else about my trepidation to give them the satisfaction of seeing the back-East girl afraid of ghosts. I was teased enough about what I was doing there.

Close to Hallowe'en I began to hear noises coming from the basement. At first I made up stories about the wind and about the house settling in the colder weather. After a while those theories did not hold. I checked every nook in the basement very carefully one day but could see no evidence of anything unusual. Yet the noises persisted, but only late at night.

On Hallowe'en night there was a terrible wind and rain storm. I heard many scary noises but refused to give in to my fear. I couldn't sleep. Near midnight I really had to go and use the pail in the basement. I grabbed my flashlight, opened the door, and slowly headed down the stairs. It was quiet. I put the light down and used the rudimentary facilities. It was then that every hair on my arms and the back of my neck stood straight up! I could hear breathing!

I froze. I listened. It was definitely breathing. I inched my hand toward the flashlight, my heart pounding. I grasped the light and whirled around toward the sound of the breathing!

I didn't have ghosts in the basement; I had goats in the basement! Billy and Annie were pinned in the spotlight.

The little darlings had found the chute that used to feed wood into the basement, and butted it open for a passage into a basement warmer than their barn. I bought more straw from the neighbours, nailed the chute closed, and was never haunted again!

I Remember Margaret

*"And nothing I cared, at my sky blue trades,
that time allows In all his tuneful turning so
few and such morning songs,"*

I WAS SITTING ROCKING ON THE PORCH watching the sunset, smelling that fall tang in the air when I remembered Margaret and getting ready for winter in Saskatchewan. That was quite a few years ago now.

I recalled that Margaret was originally from Yorkshire, England, a sheep farm there. She'd wanted to see more of the world than "stone walls and sheep's arses" and that's how she'd gotten to a little farm in eastern Saskatchewan. She'd married Sigerd Larsen when she was "past child bearin' years", as she put it.

Sigerd was the night man at the jail in town and spent most of his days sleeping and eating. Margaret fed, watered, herded, milked and loudly cursed her cattle. She mended fences, fixed frozen water pipes, put the milk through the separator and did never ending chores.

Sigerd headed into town around 10:30 p.m. and came back around 7:30 the next morning. Margaret would already be up and milking. Sigerd would get breakfast ready-porridge, scrambled eggs or French toast with home made preserves or local honey. Tea was for Margaret, coffee or hot milk for Sigerd, depending on whether he was staying up or going to bed.

Her day was made up of two rounds of milking, two rounds of barn chores, and then house or garden chores. Sigerd slept or cooked or cut wood or tinkered on the car or tractor. Margaret made biscuits, scones, endless pots of tea on the wood stove, and cut coupons for the days Sigerd would do the shopping. Margaret was not one to go to town. She never "saw much occasion to go" as she would say, and was more comfortable in the barn cursing her stubborn, stupid little herd.

Margaret's weakness was the Avon lady. She never bought make-up-never wore the stuff. No creams could ever soften her leathery calloused hands. But she did love the bottles, the porcelain and glass containers, so colourful, so delicate and beautiful. She had Christmas trees, Santas and reindeer full of aftershave; she had a lovely lady for every month of the year; she had smelly stuff in antique cars, ships, train cars, and perfume bottles of every hue and design.

She'd started collecting them in 1954 when she'd arrived in Canada. Now the whole sunporch was lined with loaded shelves and stacked boxes. Every new Avon lady to that big and challenging territory got the year by year tour when she visited Margaret for the first time.

Each one marveled at the vastness and variety of the collection.

Once Margaret came over to the shack I was staying in to help me, the back-East girl, get ready for a Saskatchewan winter. I'd traded work for a wagon load of straw bales I'd used to line the outer walls and build a shelter for my little Volkswagen.

Margaret had come to help put thick, opaque plastic sheets over the windows and between the bales and the walls. She brought her own hammer and leather carpenter's belt. I'd hold the stuff in place while she, nails protruding from her mouth, hammered and muttered and cursed. She was up and down that ladder with dogged determination. I admired her stamina, her energy, and her vocabulary, none of which I could match.

I had noticed Margaret going to work with Sigerd a couple of times and asked her over lunch if she'd gotten a job at the jail too. She clumsily explained that she and Sigerd rarely shared a bed because of "the Jesus cows". If he and she wanted to "have some time alone, if you know what I mean," she would go to the jail with him when there was no one in the three cells and they could lock the doors and spend some time together.

She hated to leave the farm alone all night but Sigerd got cantankerous enough that she agreed to the jail-house rock alternative. They would make a night of it she said, careful to swear me to secrecy lest Sigerd should "get canned". They would take a picnic basket with schnapps for Sigerd and Bailey's Cream for Margaret, have dinner and drinks, Sigerd would turn on the radio for dance music and then-Margaret giggled, and I got the idea.

Every time my foundered horse or thrill-seeking cow would wander off, it was usually Margaret on the party line to tell me, or she would walk the wayward beast home and stay for tea. When Margaret's cows made a dash for freedom, I'd help her round them up amid Margaret's creative

and incessant cursing. According to her, these poor creatures were sent by the devil to plague her life.

I once watched her help at the birthing of a calf and
saw a tender, nurturing side that she kept well hidden. She
hated to call the vet because of the cost but, on one occasion, a Cesarean delivery was inevitable. She called me to
see if I would cut the "rotten whore" open but I declined.
She paid her bills in cash after some grumpy dickering
with the local vet. Apparently, the bill was more than
either animal was worth. The vet had heard this often
before and wondered about his choice of practice.

When I was leaving to come back East, Margaret had
me over for tea and scones as she often did. She gave me
the honour of choosing one bottle from her Avon collection. I still have the old fashioned school desk with the
apple on top.

I remember she gave me a bear hug that left me
breathless. She told me she'd never had a woman to talk to
much before and had appreciated the company. She also
said that she and Sigerd had never laughed so much as at
my attempts to live in that damn shack! We both shed a
tear or two, and said our good-byes.

Back on my porch, I realized that I was getting a chill
and that it was dark enough to see the reflections of the car
lights go across the kitchen wall. I went back inside smil-
ing, remembering Margaret.

THE BOOTLEGGER

"And wake to the farm forever fled from the childless land."

L AST NIGHT I SAW THE MAGICAL BALLET of the Northern Lights flash dancing across the sky. I wondered if my buddy, Stanley, was watching them too. He had always been awed by their beauty, never tiring of watching one of the wonders of his world.

Stanley had always been a farm boy, raised on his family's Saskatchewan farm with stories of his grandparents' sod hut. He had heard about their hardships: the lack of food, the cold winters with little fuel, the back-breaking work, and five children born at home and only three surviving.

These stories put living in the Depression with dust storms and no money into perspective. Stanley learned early not to complain when he was hungry and to work hard seven days a week. He got some schooling, enough to do his figures and his letters. His two older brothers and two younger sisters filled their little house with laughter and games and horse play. When he looked back on his life, those had been the best times.

They would play cards and guessing games, sing songs, and tell stories around the kitchen table in the evenings. They'd been together then. Father was in the barn or out in the fields. Mother was in the house, sewing or cleaning or cooking. He and his brothers, Arthur and Sam, helped their father, hunted, fished, trapped and had contests of strength or wit. His sisters, Violet and Cora, laughed at their brothers' clowning. Sometimes the whole family would take a blanket out into the night, lie on it and watch the stars or the Northern Lights. These were powerful memories for Stanley.

Each child had kept animals until they couldn't afford to feed them any more. Then the dog, Speckles, was shot along with Barnaby, the old horse. They ate Barnaby stew for weeks. The other animals were sold or traded or devoured until there was nothing left but what they could carry. After nearly ten years of drought and depressed prices, the Parker family were forced to abandon the farm to the bank and walk away with only what they could carry on their backs. They left behind everything that had formed the memories and the stories that made them who they were.

They moved into the top of the blacksmith's shop in town and Stanley got his first job to pay their rent. He was the blacksmith's boy. No more mingling frosty breath with the cows in the morning, no more coyotes serenading them to sleep at night, no sudden surprises as a deer or a snowy owl burst from the bushes. The moonlight reflected on the snow was not as magical in town. The panorama of the stars was not so near.

Arthur and Sam joined the army and went to Europe to fight the Nazis. The family didn't hear from them again. One day an officer from the boys' regiment brought the bad news. That was how they heard that both boys were gone forever. They didn't even have their bodies to bury.

After the war, Violet and Cora married and moved away, one to Edmonton, and the other to Winnipeg. Stanley moved to the first of a series of hired hands' quarters, bunkhouses or back sheds. His parents didn't long survive their grief at the loss of their sons and their farm.

Stanley worked as a hired hand at one place or another across the prairies for thirty odd years. He didn't complain, had simple needs, and worked hard. He could fix anything from harness to threshers to combines, and could handle just about any kind of animal with gentleness and firmness. He was a loner; one of those lost men who had come out of the Depression and the war.

One fall night, he watched the Northern Lights explode across the wide screen of the Saskatchewan sky. The next day, he decided he wanted to go home, back to the farm where he had once had a family, had once belonged.

Stanley didn't have a car. In fact, he didn't own much of anything except his work clothes. He gave his notice after the harvest and started the one hundred mile trek to go home. He did not accept rides because he didn't know exactly what to say to anyone about his trip. So he walked. It was easier.

He knew there would be no one there to greet him. He knew it was a rather odd thing to be doing, but he was doing it. He was taking early retirement with no pension, and he was going home.

It was the crisp beginning of a prairie winter when

Stanley came home. The house and barn were gone, plowed under as if they'd never been. The joyful place in his memory was one big, flat field that somebody was still working. Over where the well used to be, he found twelve grain storage bins, abandoned and empty. They were two stories high and round with conical roofs. Inside, there was a poured concrete floor and a medium sized round room. Stanley chose one and made it his new home.

At first he found scrap to burn to keep warm at night. He found an old tin can where he hid his meager savings and another one to drink from once he got the old well working again. That's what he was doing when the Svenson brothers came by to investigate the smoke they'd seen at the old Parker place, which was now their land.

It was likely the hip flask the brothers shared that gave Stanley the idea for his next career. The Parkers had been teetotallers and Stanley was no exception. He explained his story to the Svensons and his intention to take up residence in the grain bin. They were concerned for his safety but he assured them that if his grandparents had lived there in a sod hut, he could live in a grain bin.

He did say that he was handy and was still willing to work if they needed him and, in exchange, he wanted to use their tractor to drive into town once a week. They agreed, and spread the word that there was a Parker on the old Parker place once again.

The first week, he invested in three cases of twenty-four and a case of rye. That took most of his saved-up cash. He went over to the hotel and informed every person there that they were invited out to the Parker place anytime they were thirsty. People were curious.

He nearly sold out that first week because the word spread that he sold at his cost as long as the purchaser brought a present. Canned goods, an old arm chair, an out-house and two Hudson Bay blankets arrived the first week. By the end of the month, he had a wood-burning stove, a cot, a cord of firewood, a moth-eaten rug, a kerosene lamp, dishes and cutlery. The local drinkers appreciated the twenty-four hour service and adopted Stanley in their own way.

It was the first time in a long time that Stanley had friends who cared about him and his well being. In the circle of warmth around the wood stove they played cards, sang songs, played guessing games, and had the occasional chili stew dinner. Stanley had a sort of family again.

Every week he went to town to buy his supplies. He worked for the Svensons on occasion and hosted his friends regularly. He used the other grain bins for storing garbage, old machinery parts that could come in handy someday, old furniture he might fix up someday, and just plain junk.

I first met Stanley when one of the local fellows invited me to go out for dinner one fall evening. I made the mistake of changing out of my jeans for the first time in months. We drove in his pick-up south of town and turned into a field. I began to wonder if I had made a major error in judgement, not just in wardrobe.

We parked, along with three other pick-ups, in a grassy circle of grain bins and garbage. My friend got out and knocked on the door of one of the bins The door swung open to reveal a splash of golden light. He waved at me to come in. Reluctantly, I did.

Inside a blast of hot air hit my skin. It had to be eighty some degrees Fahrenheit and the smell of spicy chili mixed with cigarette smoke and warm bodies in close quarters was almost overpowering in the little round room. I was the only female. A large toothless man sprawled on a cot, three young fellows wearing cowboy boots and hats sat on a bench clutching bottles of beer, and two older men in rumpled brown suits got up from the wooden boxes they'd been sitting on to greet me with bear hugs and garlic-whiskey breath.

I was gallantly offered one of the boxes and a steaming tin pie plate of strong smelling chili and a warm beer. The toothless Stanley introduced himself and apologized for the lack of refrigeration. I assured him I was grateful for his hospitality. He replied that a lady was always welcome on the Parker place.

I could tell that he had been a handsome man, tall, with naturally curly white hair, clear blue eyes and large, calm worker's hands. He had a gentle twinkle in his eyes and a warm smile. I liked and trusted him right away.

There followed an evening of storytelling, song, stomach cramps, laughter and as few trips as possible to the smelly outhouse. They told stories of R.C.M.P. officers coming to dinner with Stanley and their amazement when he explained about his nonprofit motive. They discussed the ethics of the Great Shit Lake Canoe Race, the wily poachers of Nut Mountain, and played a game called Name the Stupidest Politician.

I came back with my friend a few times and, sometimes on my own, to visit with Stanley and listen to his stories about his past or about the birds and animals he observed so closely. When he wasn't entertaining, Stanley was out of doors. He'd walk for miles. He knew where the fox dens were, whether the timber wolves were coming down from the north, where the owls were nesting, and how many mice there were that year compared to others.

When I came back for a visit in the spring, I found that the home bin had burned down. Cardboard and straw insulation and a wood stove pose certain risks, but Stanley was all right. He had moved into one of the other bins and his friends had again provided furnishings and household necessities. Stanley told me that he was happy to be home. He understood when I told him that I was going home, too. He gave me a big hug and a warm beer. I gave him my transistor radio so he could listen to CBC. We took the boxes outside and sat in the spring sun for our last visit.

I didn't know what I was going to do when I got back to Ontario, but I thought that if Stanley could create a home in a grain bin and a community for himself there, I'd manage too.

FOR THE BIRDS

"And honoured among foxes and pheasants"

I T WAS SUMMER IN SASKATCHEWAN. The days stretched out to the horizon and back, long hours of sunshine and farming activity. Compared to my neighbours I was not busy enough and so I decided to take on a project. The story of my life: take on another project I knew nothing about and jump in with both feet.

I found a niche market. Pheasants. They didn't have any there. They must need some. The idea was so perfect that I started immediately. No time to do any research or preparation. I had a barn. I could get feed. I had a market for specialty poultry — the neighbours. I had high hopes, and confidence in my bird raising and marketing abilities.

I called a fellow graduate of the University of Guelph who had a pheasantry in Aylmer, Ontario, and made arrangements for three dozen chicks to be flown from Toronto to Saskatoon. The initial investment.

I got two large dog cages from the vet in town where I volunteered in exchange for showers and laundry facilities. I got chick starter feed from the Co-op. I had clean straw at the farm for the animals I boarded. I arranged to pick up heat lamps from a neighbour and strung an extension cord from the house to the barn.

When I went over to pick up the heat lamps and proudly told them of my plans, I saw exchanged looks and heads shaking. It seems that the barn would be an easy target for foxes or coyotes, who would decimate my little birdies pretty quickly. Anything worth flying in from out East was worth keeping in the back kitchen.

I had to agree. My mother sent me the Strathroy Age Dispatch from home and I put that newspaper all over the floor in the room off the kitchen, struggled to carry in the cages already full of straw, set up the heat lamps, and filled the water bottles and feeders. I brought the two heavy bags of feed into the house and was ready for the arrival of the little cheepers.

I got up at 5:00 a.m. the next morning and made the two-hour drive to the airport, ready to pick up my birdie babies, more newspaper covering the back seat of my Volkswagen bug. I signed the papers and loaded two boxes of the yellow peepers and headed home. They were so cute. How would I ever be able to sell them or bring myself to kill them for food?

By the time I got home, they were pretty well covered in crap. The car never smelled quite the same again. Then they crapped all over the food dishes and didn't know how to use the water bottles. I put out water dishes but they spilled them immediately.

The next few weeks were a nightmare, bird hell. They were noisy twenty four hours a day despite the blankets I tucked around their cages every night. They finished the two big bags of food within a week, stunk to high heaven, and dirtied the straw bedding so that it had to be changed at least once a day. At first I could put them back into the boxes they came in while I cleaned the cages, but soon they were too big for that. I got another cage but they soon needed another and another. They ate, grew, crapped incessantly, and took hours of my time.

The worst was the heart of darkness in the summer kitchen — cannibalism. I woke up one early morning to four bloody bodies and crazed birds throwing themselves against the wire walls of the cages. Barbarian birds. Tearing each other apart. Pecking at their dead.

I called the vet. He said boil eggs, cool them and put them into the cages. I did. The sharp beaked birds attacked them and devoured them, shell and all. Dozens of eggs over the next few weeks. Bags of feed. More and more food. More and more money.

The smell was beginning to make me retch as I cleaned the cages. My hair and clothes smelled. That stink saturated the whole house and everything in it. Their beady little eyes followed my every move. They got feath-ers and attitudes. They bit me when I tried to clean the cages. Hitchcock must have raised pheasants. I finally understood the terror that would inspire his film.

I considered taking them to the barn and letting them take their chances with the coyotes, but I had spent too much time and money to give up now. Some had died already. My profit margin was gone. I would need about ten dollars a pound to break even. The neighbours stopped visiting. It was too noisy to talk and too smelly to stay. I knew they were chuckling about my feathered folly.

I remembered my high hopes, my fear that I could not kill my little birdies. By the end, I couldn't wait. I wanted to tear them apart with my bare hands. I wanted to see them in the freezer locker in town in plastic bags. I wanted to see their roasted bodies on platters.

The horror...the horror.

WHO REMEMBERS BILLY?

"Time held me green and dying

Though I sang in my chains like the sea."

OLD HANK DIDN'T TALK MUCH for a bartender. He pumped the draft handle, stacked the trays, washed the glasses and emptied ashtrays quickly and delicately for a man of his age and red-meat-eating Saskatchewan farmer size. He kept the cash register humming. He was the no-nonsense bouncer and bar manager, too.

I was the waitress, twenty-one and running away from Toronto and parental expectations. A small prairie town was the last place they would look for me, if they were looking, at all. I hauled trays of food and beer in the bar, ate leftovers in the kitchen of the hotel, and visited the laundromat down the block to wash my smoke-soaked clothes. I had a grungy, little room upstairs where I slept dreaming of drowning in oceans of beer. That had been my little world for the two months of summer.

I knew the drinkers in town; I knew Old Hank, the kids in the kitchen, and Anita, the native woman who looked after the laundromat. I babysat her four quiet, big-eyed kids some mornings. The drinkers were noisy and I ignored them. Hank and Anita were both quiet even when I tried to talk to them. I was getting pretty lonesome. Then I met Billy.

Billy called me "Toronto". He said that he was the Lone Ranger and I was his loyal sidekick, "Toronto". He'd come into the bar, eyes twinkling, put money in the juke-box, and we'd dance around a bit between customers. "Bee-bop-a-lula, She's my baby" was his favourite. He figured with a name like that she must be Indian like him. He'd back off the farm boys if I didn't want to dance with them.

Then he'd order a pitcher of beer, pick up his pool cue like a jousting lance, and the games would begin. He flew around the table bouncing on the balls of his feet at first. By evening and many pitchers later, he'd be lurching, stumbling, and muttering. He would lose all the money he'd won and then he'd lose his temper, too.

Old Hank had two choices when that happened: call the Mounties, Doug and Fred, or throw Billy out and keep him out by himself. If anyone tried to help Hank, Billy would fight. Hank told the fellows to leave him be and Billy went quietly for Old Hank most of the time. But if Hank left Billy drinking for too long, it was eight- ball brawl time. The joint would be hopping, pool cues swing-ing, shouting, heads up ducking and running.

The Mounties, Doug and Fred, would haul Billy out and put him in the "hoosegow" as he called it. On just a regular drunk, they'd take him to Anita's and he'd sleep it off under the folding table at the laundromat. I found out that Anita was his half sister one morning when I took my laundry in while they were there drinking coffee.

"The Lone Ranger lost his silver bullets last night,

Toronto. You've got to take better care of me, kemo sabe." That was Billy, hung over and joking still.

Sometimes Billy, Anita, and the kids would go out to the Nut Mountain Reserve to visit family. It was pretty quiet at the hotel those days. His pool cue with the crude B-I-L-Y scrawled on it would be the only reminder. Nobody touched it.

Then he'd be back, smoking, dancing, drinking, and joking between games, laughing, taunting, making bets, winning big in pin-drop suspenseful shoot outs until he was flat broke and stupid, stumbling drunk again.

One night in November, Billy got to eight-ball brawl state. Old Hank marched him outside into the snow. Billy came right back in again, and two farm boys picked him up and carried him out to the back of a pickup. He must have passed out in the back of the truck.

The next morning Sigerd Larsen brought Billy's frozen body into town. He'd found him in a ditch about a mile out, dead from exposure.

"November in Saskatchewan is no place to go for a midnight stroll," laughed the drinkers.

"Musta had a snootful last night," hooted the farm boys.

"Another dead drunk Indian."

"Another dead drunk Indian."

They said that over and over and over.

Old Hank had enough of it. I could see his neck and face getting redder and redder. Finally, he picked up Billy's pool cue and announced that the hotel was closing out of respect for Billy. They thought he was joking and started laughing, and so he chased the whole dinner crowd out of the hotel yelling, 'Get out of here, you sons-a-bitches."

Then he locked the doors. He poured himself a double rye and one for me too. I'd never seen Hank take a drink. Then he took down one of those black and white panoramic regimental photographs from beside the mirror behind the bar. He pointed to a big, moon-faced man standing in the back row and said, "That's me."

Then he pointed to a skinny, dark haired boy sitting crosslegged in the front row. "That's Billy."

Hank didn't say anything else for a long time. He was crying and drinking. Then he said, "Best goddamned sharpshooter we had. Saved my ass a couple of times. Yep. Little Billy sure could shoot."

Then he picked up Billy's pool cue and sighted along it as if he were holding a rifle. Then he hung it up over the mirror, a place of honour in a bar. If Old Hank put it there, that is where it would stay. We drank a toast to Billy and called it a night.

The next morning, I went over to help Anita with her kids. We were having a cup of coffee when she went over to a shelf and took out a shoe box. There, wrapped in tea towels, were three medals that Billy had won.

"He was proud a them," she told me in her flat, matter-of-fact way. "You give 'em to Hank. Billy said he'd give 'em to him someday."

I took them over to Hank at the bar. He unwrapped them like they were fine crystal. He put his big hand on my shoulder.

"Thanks, Toronto," he said gently.

Then he looked out over the lunch crowd, sighed and asked quietly, "Who remembers Billy?"

THE HIRED GIRL

"So it must have been after the birth
of the simple light

In the first, spinning place,
the spellbound horses walking warm

Out of the whinnying green stable

On to the fields of praise."

"SIT UP STRAIGHT AND LISTEN to what happened to Lot's wife when she didn't do what she was told, and let this story be a lesson to you all! Quit squirming over there, young lady!"

That was Miss Tilley Birdwell, and I was the "young lady" at Sunday school that morning. It was the first warm day of a Saskatchewan spring, and I was not interested in hearing Miss Flap Lips Birdwell's unimaginative, small-minded version of Bible stories.

Besides, Miss Kate had come to church — a rare occasion. I was real curious to see the woman who ran her own outfit, broke and trained fine cutting horses . I'd heard how she rode a horse like a man and often alone — "when anything could happen," my mother would say with her disapproving sigh.

That was the day Miss Kate spoke to my mother about needing help over the summer. I was in my final year at the grammar school and, as the oldest of five, I was pretty handy around the house. Miss Kate offered to pay me fifty cents a week. To my surprise, my mother agreed, even though she did not approve of Miss Kate's brazen ways.

My daddy drove me over in the buggy on Mondays, and Miss Kate brought me back on Friday afternoons. The first few weeks my mother would ask, "Rose, you aren't getting any funny ideas from that woman, are you?"

I told her, "Mama, I'm washing curtains and bedding, scrubbing walls and floors, cleaning windows, soft soaping leather, digging and weeding the garden, hauling water and wood, cooking, and all the kinds of chores I do at home."

I told her how Miss Kate took spells and that was why she'd wanted me there. She'd get pains in her chest and had trouble keeping anything in her stomach. She'd take a nap after lunch each day. Miss Kate's favourite lunch was biscuits and gravy cooked up with a mess of onions. She said my biscuits were quite substantial but she often took a spell after eating them.

Miss Kate still did the barn chores, looked after the animals, and worked in the garden. She hired a neighbour to haul and split the wood while I did most of the house work. Miss Kate expected spotless cleaning. "The more the kids, the lower the standards," my mother used to say. Miss Kate didn't have any kids and, at her age, never would.

What she did have was a personal, conversational friendship with God and a whole slough of angels. She was always talking to them and singing and clapping her hands and dancing around. She sang real joyful songs with more jump to them than the ones we sang in church.

She sang OH WHEN THE SAINTS COME MARCH- ING IN, OH WHEN THE SAINTS COME MARCHING IN! and she'd flutter her hands to GIMME THAT OLD TIME RELIGION. She taught me lots of those songs like SWING LOW, SWEET CHARIOT, COMIN' FOR TO CARRY ME HOME. And, when I'd haul in the wood, she'd be singing, BRINGING IN THE SHEAVES and laughing.

When I'd sing along, she'd clap her hands and say, "Come on and sing it like you mean it, girl!" She told me those songs were meant to be a celebration, a rejoicing in the Lord, and that she thought our church was pretty grim and that God did not intend us to be so dull. She said, "Heaven must be a lot more fun than our church, or what's the use in going there?"

I told her I wouldn't want the likes of Miss Tilley Birdwell in charge of Heaven. Miss Kate shouted, "Amen to that, Miss Rose!"

She told me, "If you need any help, just ask the angels, because they are always standing by willing to help — if only someone would ask them."

I told her to ask for help with her spells. She kind of looked at me funny and said she had, but she figured those spells were necessary somehow to prepare her for life in Heaven. She asked me if I knew I was smart and if I was planning to go on to the Senior School. I hadn't figured on it until then.

I liked Miss Kate very much and wouldn't let waggle tongues like Miss Tilley Birdwell get away with calling her strange or crazy, because she wasn't. She just had a lot of spunk! She worked me hard but treated me real well. She paid me two quarters every Friday, ate lunch with me every day, taught me about God and music and joy. She taught me how to dance. She'd hum a tune and lead me twirling around the kitchen. She taught me what to say if a gentleman came calling. She told me about her life and let me know I could live mine any way I wanted: happy or miserable, married or single, educated or ignorant. It was up to me. She was the only reason I went back to the Senior School in the fall.

The next summer I went to work for her again, seven days a week. I couldn't believe my eyes! She had shrunk! She was smaller than I was. Pain had cleft deep lines in her face. She had the spells more often now and rested in bed most afternoons.

She had sold most of the horses just to keep going. I felt real bad for her but she said, "Don't be silly, girl. I'm getting closer and closer to Heaven and that's a cause to rejoice!" She could always find a cause to rejoice.

She asked me what I'd been learning in school and allowed that most of it was useless but to stick to it anyway. She asked me to read passages from the Bible to her while she was resting. The Psalms were a favourite. Then we'd talk about God's holy garden and the glory land awaiting. We'd talk about the tussles between God and the Devil and how folks take up sides every day.

That summer I helped Miss Kate as she died and she helped me to live, to live my life the way I wanted it. We looked after each other every day. She was a gentle, brave and joyful soul and I bet God's real happy to have her back in the angel choir. She'll be up there clapping her hands and shouting out, "Sing it like you mean it!"

THE LAKE ISLE OF INNISFREE

I will arise and go now, and go to Innisfree,
And a small cabin build there, of clay and wattles made:
Nine bean-rows will I have there, a hive for the honey-bee,
And live alone in the bee-loud glade.

And I shall have some peace there, for peace comes dropping
slow,
Dropping from the veils of the morning to where the cricket
sings;
There midnight's all a glimmer, and noon a purple glow,
And evening full of the linnet's wings.

I will arise and go now, for always night and day
I hear lake water lapping with low sounds by the shore;
While I stand on the roadway, or on the pavements grey,
I hear it in the deep heart's core.

W.B. Yeats

ORDER FORM

For copies of *Under the Apple Boughs, Spiral to the Heart*
or *Sing a Song of Six Packs* send a cheque or money order to:
OASIS PUBLISHING
BOX 810, ELORA, ONTARIO, CANADA N0B 1S0
dmccaw@sentex.net

CANADIAN PRICE: $12.95   U.S. PRICE: $10.95

Under the Apple Boughs

QUANTITY _____ X PRICE @ $ _____ = _____

Spiral to the Heart

QUANTITY _____ X PRICE @ $ _____ = _____

Sing a Song of Six Packs

QUANTITY _____ X PRICE @ $ _____10.00_____ = _____

SHIPPING $ 2.50

TOTAL _____

NAME: _____

ADDRESS _____

CITY/TOWN _____

PROV./STATE_____ CODE _____

Allow 3-4 weeks delivery